RAPTAUR

MANDARIN

intro

JUDGE DREDD is the lawman of the future – judge, jury and executioner in one. His beat is Mega-City One – a sprawling megatropolis of nearly 400 million citizens, all potential criminals. Watching over them are the Judges – the ultimate law enforcers. Dredd is the guardian of the city and the greatest of its judges – in Mega-City One, he is the Law!

Now Judge Dredd faces a terrifying new foe – an alien predator known only as RAPTAUR. This murderous menace uses infra-red and x-ray vision, can shroud its presence from normal vision and psychic sight and it hunts humans! The carnivorous creature is turning the city into a killing ground and only Dredd can stop it!

BLINDED FOR A MOMENT!

BUT THEY'VE GOTTA BE HEADIN' FOR THE EXIT--

DROKK!

THE MUNCE TANK--!

SPLUDD!

SHPADOOOOSH!

AAAAH

YAAA!

-- STATION MC-TVX. PLEASE DO NOT ADJUST YOUR SET!

NOW THAT OUR, UHH, TECHNICAL PROBLEM IS RESOLVED, THIS IS CHEEVER MAHOON WELCOMING YOU BACK TO "STREET BEAT".

SHOTS HAVE BEEN HEARD FROM THE MUNICIPAL MUNCE BUILDING. I'M ON MY WAY THERE NOW.

STAY TUNED!

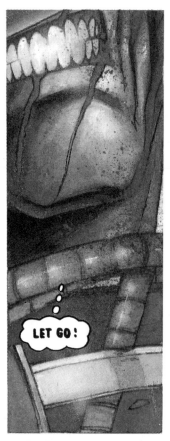

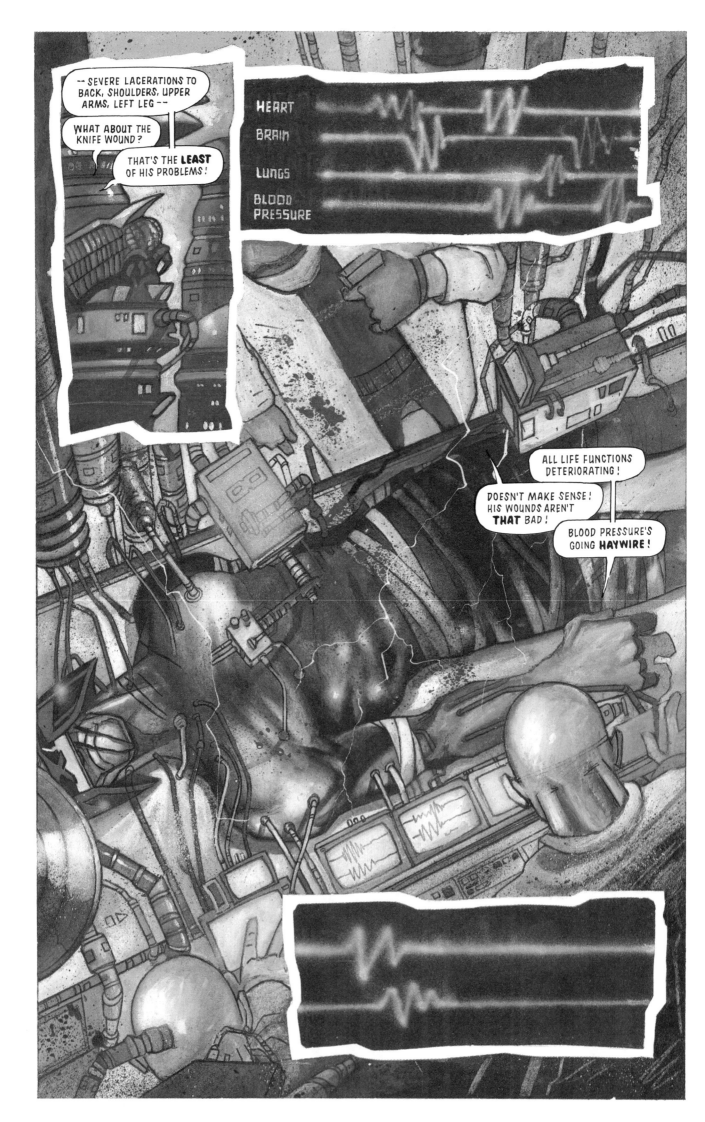

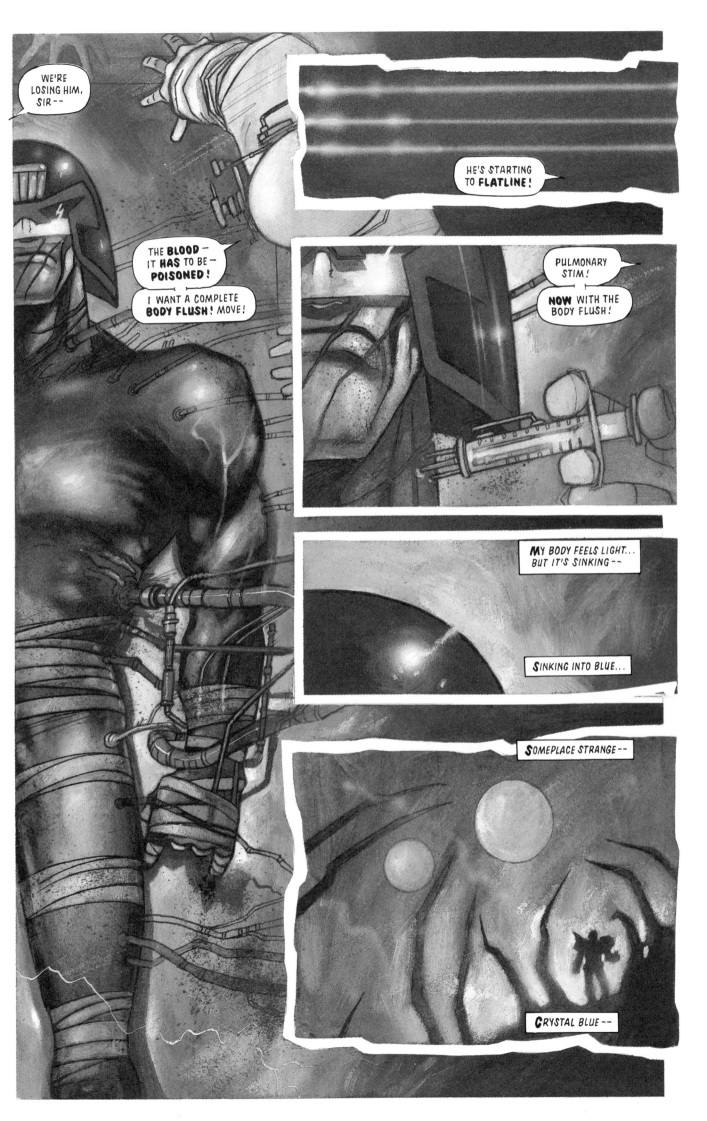

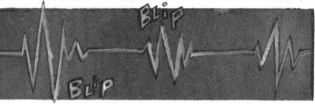

DAMN IT, DREDD! YOU'RE IN NO SHAPE FOR THIS!

TWELVE HOURS IN RAPI-HEAL'S NOT **NEARLY** ENOUGH!

RIGHT NOW, THERE'S MORE IMPORTANT BUSINESS. **MONSTER** BUSINESS!

BUT **YOU** DON'T HAVE TO BE INVOLVED! LET SOMEONE **ELSE** HANDLE IT!

YOU'VE NOTHING TO PROVE TO ANYONE!

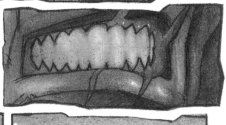

TELL ME EVERYTHING YOU KNOW ABOUT IT.

A TOTAL BLITZ ON THE TOM MOHAN BLOCK TURNED UP **17** BODIES IN SEPARATE APARTMENTS. FROM WHAT WE PIECED TOGETHER AFTER THE CITI-DEF EXPLOSION, THERE WERE AT LEAST ANOTHER **20** IN THERE.

EVIDENTLY IT **EATS** A LOT!

POST-MORTEM SHOWS THE **FIRST** CORPSE WAS KILLED THREE DAYS AGO. THOUGH MOST HAD BEEN **PART-DEVOURED**, THE FLESH OF SEVERAL WAS **UNTOUCHED**.

HOWEVER, IN **EVERY** CASE THE **SKULL** WAS CRACKED OPEN AND **BRAIN MATERIAL** REMOVED.

AT THE CITI-DEF -- THERE WAS A T.V. NEWSMAN --

CHEEVER MAHOON, WE INTERROGATED HIM. HE WAS ON SOME KIND OF STREET-BEAT SHOW. JUST **CHANCE** HE WAS THERE.

PLEASE – SEND ME SOME **MONEY.** BETTER STILL, WHY NOT **DRIVE** OVER AND **GIVE** IT TO ME IN PERSON? I'M HERE MOST NIGHTS UNTIL THE JUDGES MOVE ME ON AT DAWN!

OH SWEET GRUD--

THAT'S FAR ENOUGH, CREEP!

NEXT: **TO THE DEATH!**

MAYBE THAT'S WHY I'M HERE. TO **LAY** THE GHOST.

LIGHT ROUND THE CORNER--

SURRENDER. GIVE UP.

IGNORE THE FEELINGS! CONCENTRATE. FOCUS ON THE JOB IN HAND--

WHAT-?

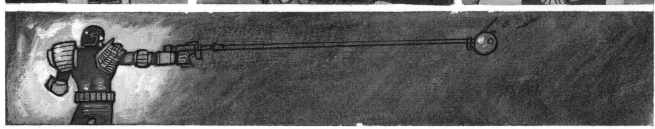

DAMN! MAHOON--!

THWIIP! WHHIIP!

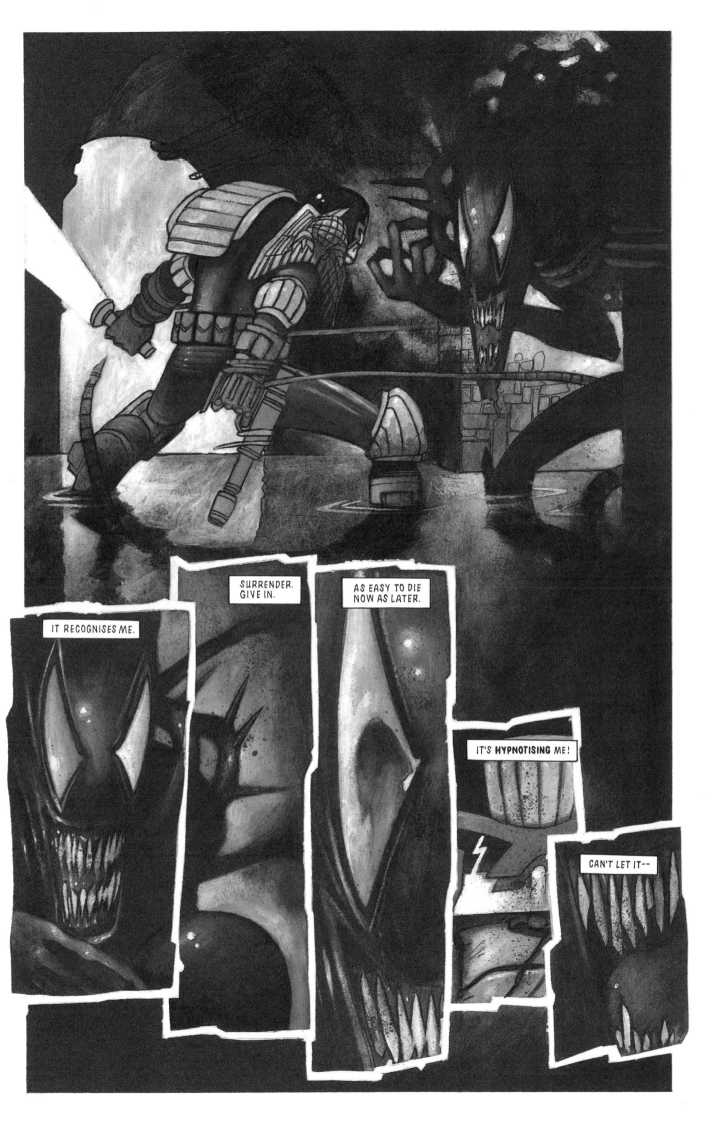

THE END